insults

with Vimrod

insults

the way you breathe really irritates me

Vimrod by Lisa Swerling and Ralph Lazar

HarperCollins*Publishers*

you are an enigma
wrapped in a riddle
cloaked in a mystery
covered by a thin layer of
pure nerd

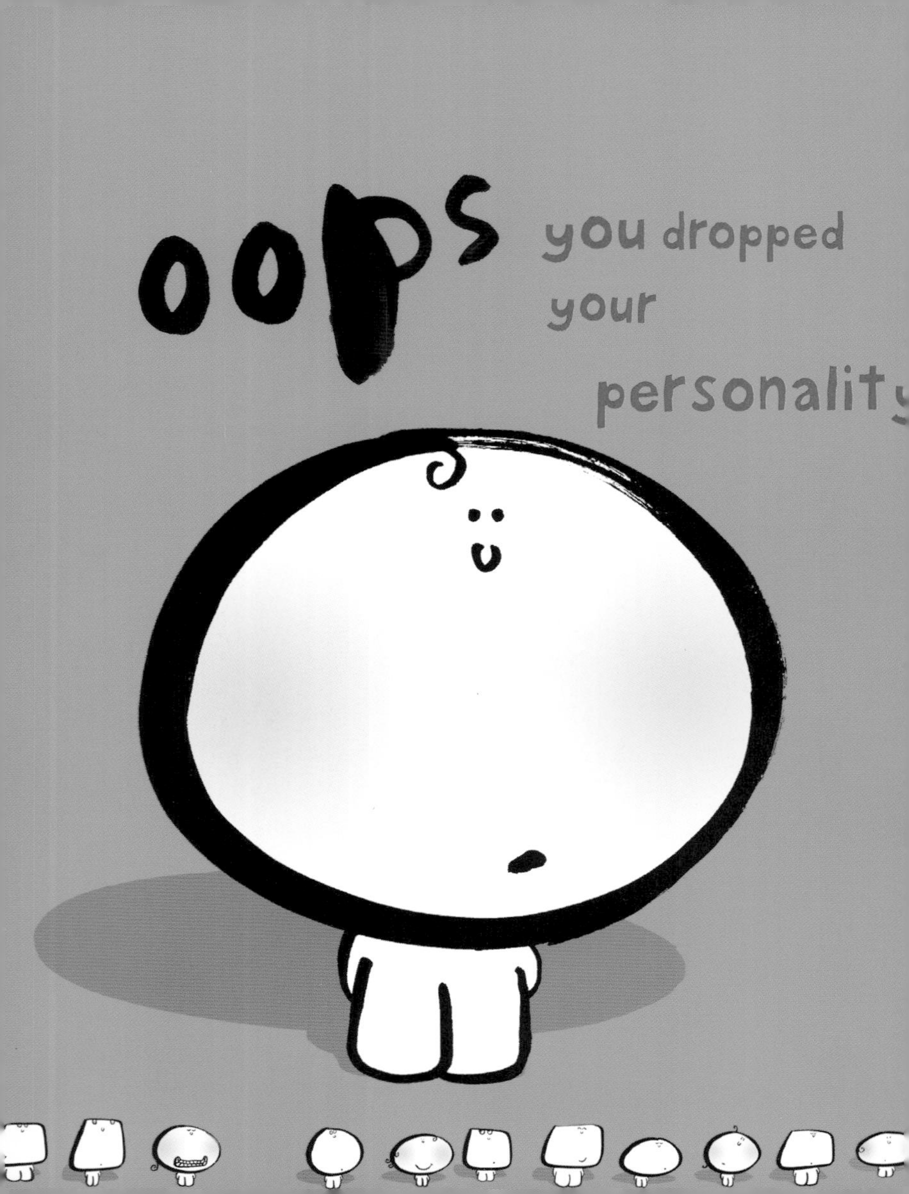
oops
you dropped
your
personalit

i find your **shadow** more engaging than you

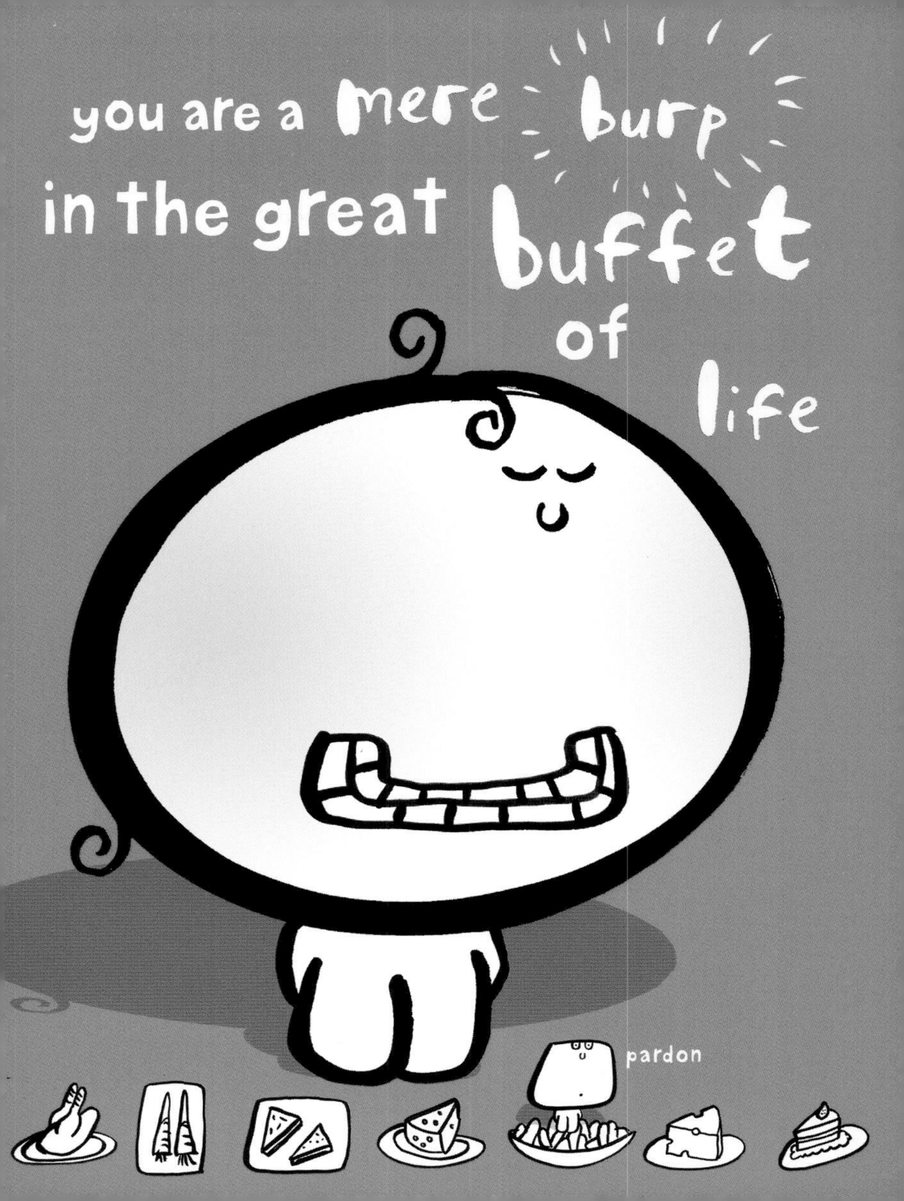
you are a mere burp
in the great buffet of life
pardon

if i invoiced
you every
time you

bugged me
i'd be rich

you should get your opinions seen to by a specialist

you are very
good at just
standing there

your lack of
self-awareness
is

inspirational

i am so busy that
i barely have the
time to ignore you

you are acting like an idiot,
which is interesting
since you
are actually
an idiot, so why the
act?

lisa swerling + ralph lazar

are two of the UK's most popular
graphic artists. Through their company
Last Lemon they have brought to life a
range of inspired cartoon characters,
including Harold's Planet, The Brainwaves,
Blessthischick and, of course, Vimrod.

writers, artists and designers, they
are married with two children, and spend
their time between London and various
beaches around the world.

HarperCollins*Publishers*
77–85 Fulham Palace Road, Hammersmith, London W6 8JB

www.harpercollins.co.uk

Published by HarperCollins*Publishers* 2007
1

A catalogue record for this book is available from the British Library
ISBN-10 0 00 725563 2
ISBN-13 978 0 00 725563 4

Set in Bokka
Printed and bound in Italy by Lego SpA

other titles in the Vimrod collection:

drink!
Wine is made to be drunk,
i am drunk,
therefore
am i wine?

Vimrod by LISA SWERLING & RALPH LAZAR

shopping
it's the little voices that tell me to go shopping

Vimrod by LISA SWERLING & RALPH LAZAR

farting
my farts hospitalise small children

Vimrod by LISA SWERLING & RALPH LAZAR

Xmas
christmas is coming run!

Vimrod by LISA SWERLING & RALPH LAZAR

chocolate
life is a struggle between good, evil and chocolate

Vimrod by LISA SWERLING & RALPH LAZAR

love
You and me... two hamsters on the spinning-wheel of life

Vimrod by LISA SWERLING and Ralph Lazar

mums
behind every great woman is her bum

Vimrod by Lisa Swerling and Ralph Lazar

dads
life is a journey between the fridge and the sofa

Vimrod

life
life is terribly long isn't it?
shall we rest?

by Lisa Swerling and Ralph Lazar